# VIVEKANANDA

NINETEENTH CENTURY INDIA. THE SPIRIT OF HINDUISM LAY HIDDEN UNDER A DEBRIS OF RITUALS — RITUALS DISOWNED BY THE INDIAN INTELLECTUALS AND SCORNED BY THE RULING BRITISH. AT SUCH A TIME WAS BORN TO VISHWANATH DATTA AND BHUVANESHWARI OF CALCUTTA, A SON WHOM THEY NAMED NARENDRANATH.

WHEN THE DOLL WAS TAKEN AWAY FROM HIM —
GIVE IT BACK.

BUT HIS MOTHER KNEW OF A WAY TO CONTROL HIM.
SHIVA, SHIVA.

THE MAGIC OF THE NAME IMMEDIATELY QUIETENED NARENDRANATH.
THERE! NOW YOU ARE CALM LIKE SHIVA IN MEDITATION.

NARENDRANATH WAS A BORN LEADER, NOT ONLY TO HIS TWO BROTHERS AND TWO SISTERS, BUT TO ALL THE NEIGHBOURHOOD CHILDREN.
I AM THE KING. YOU, MY PRIME MINISTER; AND YOU, THE JESTER.

A KING NEEDS REVENUE. YOU BRING ME SWEETS. YOU...BRING ME MARBLES...

* WANDERING MONK.

* A REFORMIST SECT FOUNDED BY RAJA RAM MOHAN ROY.

* A PLACE FOUR MILES TO THE NORTH OF CALCUTTA.

WHEN NAREN WENT TO DAKSHINESHWAR TO MEET RAMAKRISHNA —
AH, YOU HAVE COME AT LAST! WHY DID YOU KEEP ME WAITING SO LONG?
HE TALKS AS IF HE KNOWS ME.

I KNOW YOU. YOU ARE NARAYANA, COME DOWN TO HELP HUMANITY.
WHAT DOES HE MEAN? I AM VISHWANATH DATTA'S SON.

LATER, NAREN ASKED HIM THE QUESTION THAT HAUNTED HIM DAY AND NIGHT.
SIR, HAVE YOU SEEN GOD?
OF COURSE. I SEE HIM MORE CLEARLY THAN I SEE YOU. YOU CAN ALSO SEE HIM.
NAREN, THE WESTERN-EDUCATED RATIONALIST FOUND IT HARD TO BELIEVE THIS.

LATER, WHEN MITRA AND HE WERE RETURNING HOME —
WHAT DO YOU THINK OF RAMAKRISHNA?
I DON'T KNOW. I LIKE THE PLACE. I LIKE THE MAN. I WILL COME AGAIN.

A FEW DAYS LATER—
NAREN, NEXT SATURDAY I'LL BE GOING TO DAKSHINESHWAR.
I WILL JOIN YOU.

ON THEIR WAY TO DAKSHINESHWAR—
NAREN, DO YOU ACCEPT ALL THAT RAMA-KRISHNA SAYS?
NO. HOW CAN I?

THE FACE OF THE MAN WHO HAD SEEN GOD, HAUNTED NAREN. HE BEGAN VISITING DAKSHINESHWAR FREQUENTLY. ONE DAY—
NAREN, WHY DO YOU SMILE? MAY I SHARE YOUR JOKE?
SHH!

WHEN RAMAKRISHNA SAT ON THE BED AS USUAL, HE GOT UP WITH A START.
OH, IT'S BURNING! MY WHOLE BODY IS BURNING.

WHO PUT THIS SILVER COIN UNDER MY MATTRESS?
I DID. YOU HAD SAID YOU COULDN'T STAND THE TOUCH OF MONEY. I WANTED TO TEST YOU.

VISHWANATH DATTA THOUGHT THAT THE MEETING WITH RAMAKRISHNA MADE HIS SON EVEN MORE RESTLESS.
NAREN, I WANT YOU TO MARRY AND SETTLE DOWN. I HAVE CHOSEN A GIRL FOR YOU.
MARRIAGE IS NOT YET FOR ME, FATHER!

A FEW DAYS LATER, BHUVANESHWARI CAME TO VISHWANATH WITH A SUGGESTION.
WE ARE GOING THROUGH HARD TIMES. I THINK NAREN SHOULD GET A JOB AND HELP YOU.
HAVE PATIENCE, MY DEAR. I EXPECT GREAT THINGS OF HIM.

VISHWANATH DATTA DID NOT LIVE LONG ENOUGH TO SEE HIS HOPES FULFILLED.
NOW THAT FATHER IS DEAD, I HAVE TO LOOK AFTER THE FAMILY. I MUST HAVE A STEADY INCOME.

BUT HE COULD NOT GET A JOB FOR MANY WEEKS.
WHAT SHALL I DO? I'LL GO TO DAKSHINESHWAR. PERHAPS . . .

WHEN HE WENT TO DAKSHINESHWAR —
NAREN, WHY ARE YOU SO PALE? ARE YOU ILL?
TELL ME SOMETHING! DOES YOUR MOTHER KALI GIVE YOU EVERYTHING YOU ASK FOR?

YES, EVERYTHING. IF YOU WANT SOMETHING, JUST GO UP AND ASK HER.
I WANT MONEY FOR MY FAMILY.

WHEN NAREN VISITED THE TEMPLE, HOWEVER —
MOTHER! I SEEK TRUE KNOWLEDGE.

WHEN HE CAME BACK TO RAMAKRISHNA —
DID YOU SEE MY MOTHER? HOW MUCH MONEY DID YOU ASK FOR?
I COULD NOT ASK HER FOR MONEY.

RAMAKRISHNA SENT HIM AGAIN TO KALI'S TEMPLE.
MOTHER, MAY I EVER BE DEVOTED TO YOU.
AGAIN, RAMKRISHNA SENT HIM BACK AND THIS TIME HE ASKED FOR RENUNCIATION.

LATER —
I DO NOT WANT MONEY. YOU KNOW WHAT I WANT.
YES, I KNOW. LOOK INTO MY FACE.
RAMAKRISHNA TOUCHED HIM WITH HIS FOOT AND . . .

. . . THE WHOLE WORLD SEEMED TO EXPLODE INTO LIGHT. THERE WAS NOTHING BUT LIGHT, ILLUMINATING HIS CONSCIOUSNESS TO THE VERY DEPTHS.

NAREN SEEMED TO BE IN A DAZE TODAY.
YES, I SHOWED HIM THE WHOLE OF CREATION.

SOON AFTERWARDS, NAREN GOT A TEMPORARY JOB AS THE HEADMASTER OF A SMALL SCHOOL.

ONE DAY —
I MUST GO TO HIM. I CANNOT RESIST THE PULL.

AFTER HIS FIRST SPIRITUAL EXPERIENCE , NAREN WAS A CHANGED MAN. AT DAKSHINESHWAR —

I WANT TO BE ABSORBED IN GOD ALL THE TIME.
DON'T BE IMPATIENT, NAREN.

HE BEGAN SPENDING MORE TIME WITH RAMAKRISHNA, WHO WAS THEN UNDER MEDICAL OBSERVATION AT A HOUSE IN NORTH CALCUTTA. ONE DAY—
NAREN! NAREN! WHY DON'T YOU ANSWER ME?

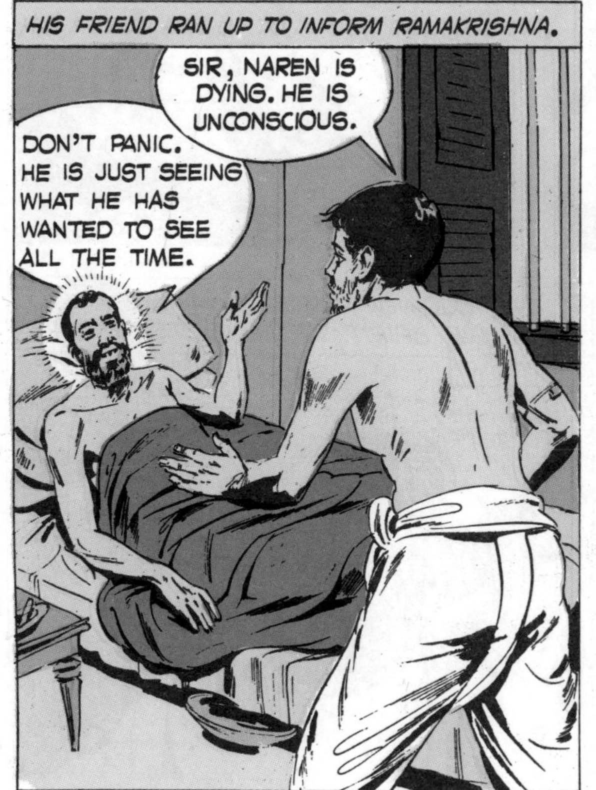
HIS FRIEND RAN UP TO INFORM RAMAKRISHNA.
SIR, NAREN IS DYING. HE IS UNCONSCIOUS.
DON'T PANIC. HE IS JUST SEEING WHAT HE HAS WANTED TO SEE ALL THE TIME.

AFTER A WHILE, WHEN NAREN ENTERED SHRI RAMAKRISHNA'S ROOM —
REMEMBER! WHAT YOU SAW WILL BE LOCKED UP LIKE A JEWEL. I'LL GIVE YOU THE KEY AFTER YOU FINISH THE MOTHER'S WORK IN THE WORLD.

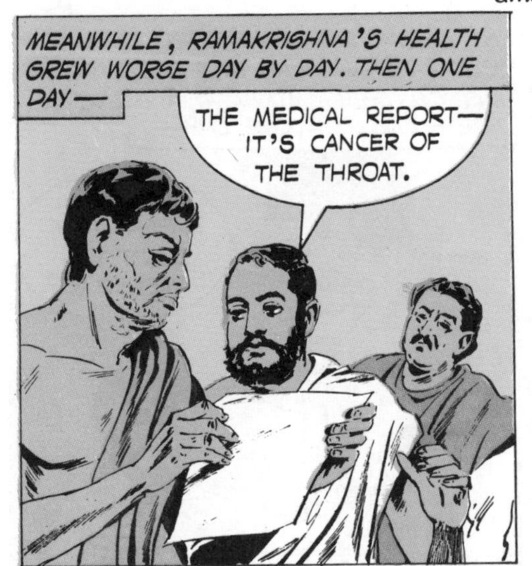
MEANWHILE, RAMAKRISHNA'S HEALTH GREW WORSE DAY BY DAY. THEN ONE DAY—
THE MEDICAL REPORT— IT'S CANCER OF THE THROAT.

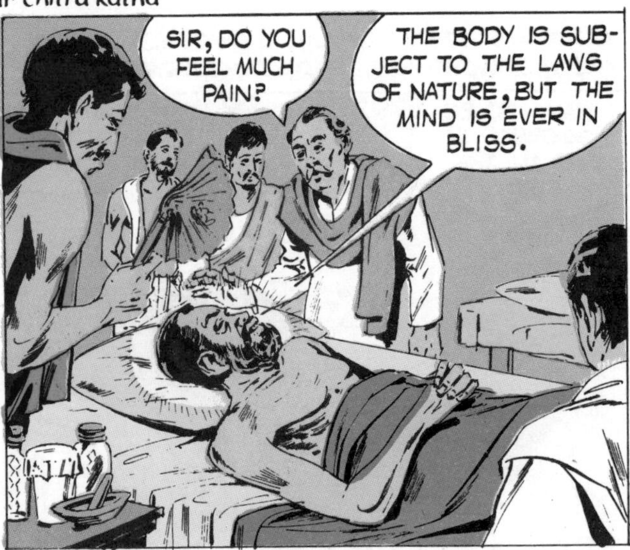
SIR, DO YOU FEEL MUCH PAIN?
THE BODY IS SUBJECT TO THE LAWS OF NATURE, BUT THE MIND IS EVER IN BLISS.

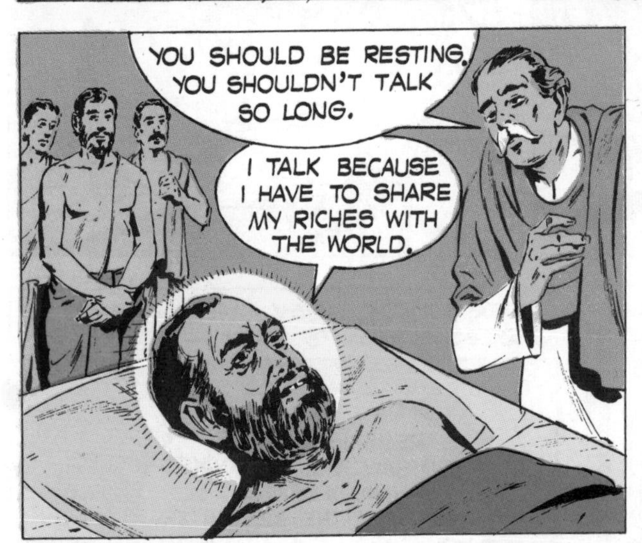
YOU SHOULD BE RESTING. YOU SHOULDN'T TALK SO LONG.
I TALK BECAUSE I HAVE TO SHARE MY RICHES WITH THE WORLD.

SOME MONTHS LATER—
NAREN, WHY DO YOU LOOK SO SAD? DON'T YOU KNOW THIS IS WHAT MOTHER WANTS?

MY TIME HAS COME. NAREN, I GIVE YOU ALL THAT I HAVE.

AT THE TOUCH OF RAMAKRISHNA, NAREN FELT THE DIVINE SPIRIT OF THE MASTER ENTERING HIM.

* SRI RAMAKRISHNA'S WIFE

THUS THE SANYASI WITH STAFF IN HAND, STARTED ON HIS PILGRIMAGE.
I MUST TRAVEL FROM NORTH TO SOUTH, EAST TO WEST. I MUST KNOW MY LAND AND MY PEOPLE.

WHEREVER HE WENT, PEOPLE RUSHED TO HEAR HIM SPEAK.
IN THE NAME OF RENUNCIATION, YOU HAVE BECOME LETHARGIC. IN THE NAME OF AHIMSA, YOU ARE PRACTISING COWARDICE. BE ACTIVE; BE BRAVE!

ONE DAY, AS HE WAS RESTING AFTER A LONG DAY'S JOURNEY, IN A FOREST—
A TIGER! I MUST FIGHT HIM. I CAN USE MY STICK. PERHAPS...
...BUT HE IS HUNGRY I AM HIS FOOD. CAN HE BE DENIED HIS RIGHT?

THE TIGER LOOKED AT HIM AND SLOWLY WENT AWAY.
THE MASTER WANTS ME TO LIVE FOR HIS WORK.

DURING HIS LONG TRAVELS IN INDIA, HE KNEW MANY MEN.
NO, SWAMIJI. DON'T USE MY HOOKAH! I AM AN UNTOUCHABLE.

HE WOULD SLEEP IN THE HUTS OF PARIAHS . . .
. . . AND CONVERSE ON EQUAL TERMS WITH MAHARAJAS.

ONE DAY, AT THE ROYAL COURT OF ALWAR —
WELCOME, SWAMIJI. WE ARE WAITING FOR YOU.
GOD BLESS YOU!

THE YOUNG, WESTERNISED MAHARAJA WAS A SCEPTIC.
SWAMIJI, YOU TALK OF GOD. DO YOU BELIEVE IN THE STONE GODS IN THE TEMPLES?
YES.

BUT HOW CAN GOD BE A THING MADE OF STONE?

SWAMIJI TURNED TO THE PRIME MINISTER.
PLEASE TAKE DOWN THAT PICTURE OF THE MAHARAJA AND GIVE IT TO ME.

WHEN THE MINISTER DID SO —
NOW SPIT ON IT! IT IS NOT THE MAHARAJA.
OH, NO. HOW CAN I?

SWAMIJI TURNED TO THE MAHARAJA.
DO YOU SEE MY POINT NOW? THE STONE GOD IS LIKE YOUR PORTRAIT— A SYMBOL. IT HELPS THE COMMON PEOPLE.

AT MOUNT ABU, HE WAS INVITED TO DINNER BY A MUSLIM OFFICER.
HOW DID YOU ACCEPT MY INVITATION, SWAMIJI? I AM A MUSLIM.
I KNOW NO CASTE OR CREED.

FROM ABU HE WENT TO GUJARAT. AT PORBANDAR, THE PRIME MINISTER OF THE STATE WAS IMPRESSED BY THE TEACHINGS OF SWAMIJI.
SWAMIJI, YOU OUGHT TO GO TO THE WEST. TAKE TO THEM THE VALUES OF HINDUISM WHICH THEY HAVE MISSED FOR ITS SUPERSTITIONS.

*ONE WHO REJOICES IN WISDOM

FAREWELL — MY COUNTRY! I SHALL TRY TO BE YOUR WORTHY SPOKESMAN.

AFTER A LONG JOURNEY VIA SINGAPORE AND JAPAN, HE REACHED CHICAGO IN JULY.

IT WAS NOT EASY FOR HIM TO FIND HIS WAY IN THAT BUSTLING CITY.
WHO ARE YOU?
I COME FROM INDIA. I WANT TO BE A DELEGATE TO THE WORLD PARLIAMENT OF RELIGIONS.
DON'T YOU KNOW, THE PARLIAMENT HAS BEEN POSTPONED TO SEPTEMBER? BESIDES, YOU HAVE TO BE SPONSORED BY AN ORGANISATION TO BE A DELEGATE.

BUT VIVEKANANDA DID NOT WORRY.
I AM HERE AMONG THE CHILDREN OF THE SON OF MARY. LORD JESUS WILL HELP ME.

ON THE TRAIN WHICH TOOK HIM FROM CHICAGO TO BOSTON, HE MET MISS KATE SANBORN.
I TOO AM GOING TO BOSTON. YOU ARE WELCOME TO STAY AT MY RESIDENCE.
THANK YOU, SISTER.
THE INVITATION CAME AS A BOON TO SWAMIJI BECAUSE HE HAD LITTLE MONEY LEFT WITH HIM.

AT MISS SANBORN'S HOME, ONE DAY —
PROFESSOR WRIGHT IS HERE TO SEE YOU.

WHEN VIVEKANANDA EXPLAINED HIS DIFFICULTY TO PROFESSOR J.H. WRIGHT —
SWAMIJI, ASKING YOU FOR YOUR CREDENTIALS IS LIKE ASKING THE SUN ABOUT ITS RIGHT TO SHINE.

PROFESSOR WRIGHT WROTE TO THE SELECTION COMMITTEE OF THE PARLIAMENT.
HERE IS A MAN MORE LEARNED THAN ALL OUR LEARNED PROFESSORS PUT TO-GETHER. I FEEL...
THE CREDENTIALS WERE ACCEPTED, AND VIVEKANANDA LEFT FOR CHICAGO.

BUT AT CHICAGO, AS ILL-LUCK WOULD HAVE IT, HE LOST HIS PAPERS.
WHAT SHALL I DO NOW?

CAN YOU TELL ME THE WAY TO THE PARLIAMENT OF RELIGIONS?
PARLIAMENT? WHAT PARLIAMENT? MAYBE YOU'RE IN THE WRONG CITY, STRANGER.

TOWARDS EVENING, FINDING AN EMPTY WAGON IN THE RAILROAD FREIGHT YARD, HE ENTERED IT...

...AND SPENT THE NIGHT THERE.
A SANYASI IS NOT BOTHERED BY DISCOMFORT!

NEXT MORNING —
HEY, YOU NIGGER! THIS IS NO PLACE TO SLEEP! GET OUT!

THE INSULT STUNG HIM.

IS THIS THE FATE OF MY MISSION TO THE WEST? I HAVE LOST THE ADDRESS OF THE PARLIAMENT OF RELIGIONS AND ALL THE MONEY I HAD.
1885

HE WALKED UP TO MANY A HOUSE ALONG THE FASHIONABLE STREETS OF CHICAGO AND MET WITH MANY A REBUFF.

WILL YOU PLEASE GIVE ME SOMETHING TO EAT?
GO AWAY.

AT LAST, OBSERVING ALL THIS FROM A WINDOW OF HER APARTMENT, MRS. HALE, A KIND OLD LADY, CAME DOWN TO MEET HIM.
YOUNG MAN, YOU SEEM TO BE IN TROUBLE CAN I HELP YOU?

WHEN VIVEKANANDA EXPLAINED HIS DIFFICULTIES —
PLEASE COME HOME WITH ME.

AFTER HE HAD EATEN . . .

. . . AND RESTED, SHE TOOK HIM TO THE OFFICE OF THE PARLIAMENT.

AT THE PARLIAMENT OF RELIGIONS, THE OFFICIAL DELEGATES FROM INDIA RESENTED HIS PRESENCE THERE.
WHOEVER IS THIS SWAMI?
WHO CARES? ALL I KNOW IS THAT THESE SANYASIS GIVE OUR COUNTRY A BAD NAME.

AFTER THE LONG-WINDED SPEECHES CAME VIVEKANANDA'S TURN.
YOU MAY SPEAK NOW, SIR.

MASTER, GIVE ME COURAGE! THIS IS THE HOUR OF INDIA'S DESTINY!

* HINDU GODDESS OF WISDOM.

VIVEKANANDA WENT FROM ONE PLACE TO ANOTHER AND SPOKE WHENEVER REQUESTED TO DO SO.

HIS LECTURES WOULD DRAW LARGE CROWDS.

WE ARE THE CHILDREN OF GOD, THE SHARERS OF IMMORTAL BLISS, HOLY AND PERFECT BEINGS ... COME UP, O LIONS, AND SHAKE OFF THE DELUSION THAT YOU ARE SHEEP! YOU ARE SOULS IMMORTAL, SPIRITS FREE, BLEST AND ETERNAL.

ONE DAY IN TEXAS, INSTIGATED BY SOME FANATIC CHRISTIANS, THE AUDIENCE BECAME ROUGH. THEY MADE HIM STAND ON A BARREL AND SPEAK.
HE IS AN ATHEIST WHO DOES NOT BELIEVE IN HIMSELF! THE OLD RELIGIONS SAID THAT HE WAS AN ATHEIST WHO DID NOT BELIEVE IN GOD! THE NEW RELIGION TELLS YOU THAT HE IS AN ATHEIST WHO DOES NOT BELIEVE IN HIMSELF!
LET'S SEE IF HE PRACTISES WHAT HE PREACHES.
YEAH! YEAH!

HE WAS PELTED WITH TOMATOES AND EGGS. SOME EVEN TOOK OUT THEIR PISTOLS AND FIRED SHOTS IN THE AIR.
THE HISTORY OF THE WORLD IS THE HISTORY OF A FEW MEN WHO HAD FAITH IN THEMSELVES. THAT FAITH CALLS OUT THE DIVINITY WITHIN. YOU CAN DO ANYTHING!
HA! HA!
RUN FOR YOUR LIFE, MAN!

BUT VIVEKANANDA WAS UNPERTURBED. THE CROWD WAS AMAZED.
YOU FAIL ONLY WHEN YOU DO NOT STRIVE SUFFICIENTLY TO MANIFEST INFINITE POWER.
MY GOD, THIS MAN HAS COURAGE.
I AM BEGINNING TO SEE WHAT HE MEANS.

*IT WAS AROUND THIS TIME THAT HIS FAMOUS WORK, RAJA YOGA WAS WRITTEN.

HE FIRST REACHED COLOMBO ON JANUARY 15, 1897. THE WELCOME THERE WAS WARM, TRIUMPHANT AND TUMULTUOUS. THOUSANDS FLUNG THEMSELVES ON THE GROUND TO TOUCH HIS FEET.

HIS DEPARTURE FROM INDIA WAS UNANNOUNCED; HIS RETURN, A NATIONAL EVENT. AT RAMNAD, SOME EAGER MEN REMOVED THE HORSES FROM HIS CARRIAGE AND PULLED IT THEMSELVES. THE RAJA OF RAMNAD WAS ONE OF THEM.

THE WORDS HE SPOKE AT RAMNAD STIRRED THE SOUL OF THE NATION.
THE SLEEPING CORPSE APPEARS TO BE AWAKENING ... INDIA, THIS MOTHERLAND OF OURS, FROM DEEP, LONG SLEEP ... NEVER IS SHE GOING TO SLEEP ANY MORE! NO OUTSIDE POWERS CAN HOLD HER BACK ANY MORE! FOR THE INFINITE GIANT IS RISING TO HER FEET!

FROM RAMNAD TO MADRAS AND TO CALCUTTA, WHEREVER HE WENT, THE CROWDS YEARNED TO HAVE A GLIMPSE OF HIM. THE YOUNG MEN OF THE COUNTRY WERE INSPIRED BY HIS WORDS.
NONE IS REALLY WEAK... STAND UP! ASSERT YOURSELF, PROCLAIM THE GOD WITHIN YOU! DO NOT DENY HIM! ARISE! AWAKE! AND STOP NOT TILL THE GOAL IS REACHED!

VIVEKANANDA ORGANISED HIS FELLOW SANYASIS INTO A DEDICATED BAND OF SPIRITUAL AND SOCIAL WORKERS. THEY NURSED THE SICK, FED THE POOR...

...AND RENDERED HELP TO THE NEEDY DURING FAMINES AND FLOODS.

ONE DAY, A VISITOR FROM ENGLAND ARRIVED.
SWAMIJI, REMEMBER ME? I AM MARGARET. I HAVE COME TO DEDICATE MYSELF TO YOU AND TO YOUR GREAT MISSION.

YOU SHALL BE CALLED NIVEDITA— THE DEDICATED ONE.

NIVEDITA LEARNT A GREAT DEAL ABOUT INDIA AND ITS CUSTOMS, THEN SET UP A SCHOOL.

MEANWHILE, VIVEKANANDA TRAVELLED ALL OVER INDIA REVIVING THE SPIRIT OF HINDUISM.
UNTOUCHABILITY MUST GO! WIPE OFF THIS BLOT! GIVE UP PRIDE OF BIRTH! SEE GOD IN ALL AND SERVE ALL!

MANY DISCIPLES CAME FROM ABROAD. HE TOOK THEM WITH HIM DURING HIS TRAVELS. ONE DAY, AT AMARNATH, IN THE HIMALAYAS—
THERE IS THE CAVE! JAI BABA AMARNATH!

WHILE IN THE CAVE, VIVEKANANDA HAD A VISION OF SHIVA AND INFINITE ENERGY FILLED HIS BEING.

HE CAME BACK TRANSFORMED.
I MUST HURRY... I HAVE WORK TO DO BEFORE I DIE! I KNOW I WILL DIE BEFORE I AM FORTY.

WHILE IN CALCUTTA, HE FORMALLY CONSECRATED THE RAMAKRISHNA MONASTERY AT BELUR AS THE HEAD-QUARTERS OF THE RAMAKRISHNA ORDER.

AND THEN PAID A VISIT TO THE SPIRITUAL CENTRES ESTABLISHED BY HIM IN THE WEST.

MEANWHILE, THE RAMAKRISHNA ORDER DEVOTED ITSELF TO THE SERVICE OF THE POOR.
ALAS, IN OUR COUNTRY THE POOR REMAIN WRETCHED. BUT THEY ARE THE BACKBONE OF OUR NATION.

THEY FED THE POOR, MANY OF WHOM WERE SANTHAL TRIBALS.

WHY DO YOU FUSS SO MUCH OVER THOSE SANTHALS?
THEY ARE AS MUCH THE CHILDREN OF GOD AS YOU OR I.

HIS HEALTH HAD BEGUN TO FAIL. ON JULY 4, 1902, HE PARTOOK OF THE NOON MEAL WITH HIS DISCIPLES.

AT SEVEN O'CLOCK IN THE EVENING THE BELL RANG FOR WORSHIP.
PLEASE GO AND ATTEND THE PRAYERS.
DING TING

HE WENT TO HIS ROOM.
NONE SHOULD COME TO ME, UNLESS CALLED FOR.

HE SPENT AN HOUR IN MEDITATION.

THEN HE CALLED THE DISCIPLE WHO ATTENDED ON HIM AND LAY QUIETLY IN BED.
BY THE TIME THE OTHERS CAME, HE HAD CAST OFF HIS BODY. HE HAD A DIVINE EXPRESSION ON HIS FACE. HE WAS NOT YET FORTY.

TODAY, A MAGNIFICENT MEMORIAL STANDS AT KANYAKUMARI, AT THE VERY SPOT WHERE, MANY YEARS AGO, HE HAD DISCOVERED HIS LIFE'S TWIN MISSION OF ELEVATING THE MASSES OF HIS COUNTRY AND PREACHING INDIA'S UNIVERSAL, SPIRITUAL MESSAGE ABROAD.